Punctuation Matters
Book 1

It is intended that this book should be used to reinforce key skills as recommended in the English National Curriculum at Key Stage 2 and in the National Literacy Strategy.

CONTENTS

by Hilda King

Hilda King Educational, Ashwells Manor Drive, Penn, Buckinghamshire HP10 8EU

Typeset by: Penn Secretarial Services
Illustrations by: Brian Watson
Printed by: Watkiss Studios

First Published 1998
Reprinted 1999
Reprinted 2001

ISBN 1 873533 50 0

Capital letters and full stops

> **A sentence begins with a capital letter and ends with a full stop. It always has at least one verb.**

When you write your own sentences, always remember these rules.

e.g. We like to take our dog for a walk.

Add capital letters and full stops to each sentence below.

1. my cat likes to drink milk

    ....

2. we often go camping in the holidays

    ....

3. there are thirty children in my class

    ....

4. it was too cold to swim in the sea

    ....

5. we think that there are mice in our loft

    ....

6. one day we all went for a bicycle ride

    ....

7. sometimes it snows in winter

    ....

8. my friend cut her finger on the knife

    ....

9. we had a lovely time at the fair

    ....

10. it is dangerous to play with matches

    ....

11. we are going for a long walk today

    ....

12. my sister likes to use the computer

    ....

Capital letters and full stops

Remember:
a sentence begins with a capital letter and ends with a full stop.
It always has at least one verb.
e.g. Tidy your room. Zak is coming to stay.

Add capital letters and full stops to make *two* sentences in each line.

1. it is too late you cannot go out now

....

2. turn the music down it is too loud

....

3. it is cold today we will need our coats

....

4. the horse stepped on my foot it broke my toe

....

5. my friend is coming home today we are going to meet her

....

6. blow out the match it will burn your finger

....

7. we did our homework we played football later

....

8. put the ice cream in the fridge it will melt

....

9. my pen is blue his pen is black

....

10. our dog was naughty he chewed my slipper

....

11. today is a holiday we hope that it will not rain

....

12. i looked out of the window i saw a fox in the garden

....

Capital letters and full stops

Remember:
a sentence begins with a capital letter and ends with a full stop.
It always has at least one verb.

Add capital letters and full stops to the sentences below.
There are two sentences in *some* of the examples.

1. there are many books on the shelf

....

2. we are late we must run to catch the train

....

3. it is a lovely day today and the sun is shining

....

4. the telephone is ringing it could be my friend calling

....

5. we went to see a ghost film we were all frightened

....

6. our team won the cup we were very pleased

....

7. my grandma is very helpful and kind

....

8. the class went jogging to keep fit

....

9. the doctor came to see my sister she had chickenpox

....

10. my brother spilt some ink on the carpet my mother was cross

....

11. the headteacher read a poem it was very funny

....

12. the ambulance went past the blue light was flashing

....

Capital letters and full stops

Below are four sentences. Rewrite them, putting in the capital letters and the full stops.

elephants have trunks they do not use their trunks like straws they fill only the tips of their trunks with water they spray the water into their mouths

....

....

....

Below are four more sentences. Rewrite them, putting in the capital letters and the full stops.

a whale is a mammal there are eighty kinds of whale an adult sperm whale may have a brain which weighs nine kilograms we do not know if this means that the whale is very clever

....

....

....

....

....

Below are five sentences. Rewrite them, putting in the capital letters and the full stops.

the moon is smaller than the sun it looks as big as the sun because it is closer to us the moon is even smaller than the earth it takes almost a month for the moon to go round the earth we get the word month from the word moon

....

....

....

....

....

....

....

Capital letters and full stops

> **Remember:**
> the word 'I' is always a capital letter.
> e.g. I want to go swimming.

Below are some sentences. Rewrite them with 'I' instead of 'i' and put in the capital letters and full stops.

1. the book i want to borrow is not on the shelf

....

2. he told me that i was good at football

....

3. that is the game i would like for my computer

....

4. i ran very fast in the race

....

5. i told my friend that i could go to her house for tea

....

6. you know that i am good at ice skating

....

7. if i buy a bag of popcorn i can share it with you

....

8. i need a drink because i am thirsty

....

9. i love to ride on the roller coaster and the big wheel

....

10. i have a large collection of marbles

....

11. my brother said that i could ride his new bicycle

....

12. i like to watch the dolphins jump

....

Capital letters and full stops

Remember:
the word 'I' is always a capital letter.

Change the 'you' to 'I' and add the capital letters and full stops. There are two sentences in *some* of the examples.

1. you can go to the park when it stops raining

....

2. you always wear blue shoes

....

3. you must hurry you might be late for the dentist

....

4. you can go to the party

....

5. he read that book you read it first

....

6. you love cakes she likes cheese

....

7. you must not forget the way you have to turn right at the fire station

....

8. you must not shout

....

9. you made a very good poster for the school disco

....

10. you overslept and you missed the train

....

11. you caught a huge fish it won the prize

....

12. you must not jump in the water it is very deep

....

Capital letters and full stops

> **Remember:**
> always use a capital letter for a name, e.g. James, Carol.

Add capital letters and full stops to make *two* sentences in each line.

1. i put on my music john did not like it

....

2. we went to the fair I had a ride with shahab on the dodgems

....

3. i go to school on the bus ann walks to school

....

4. please come to my house it is harry's birthday

....

5. i had lunch with gill david did not

....

6. the bell rang maria ran to open the door

....

7. linda began to play the trumpet peter left the room

....

8. my friend sarah has two hamsters they have very sharp teeth

....

9. i am going skating janet said that she would come too

....

10. that house is said to have a ghost cheryl and i do not believe in ghosts

....

11. marcus loves fish chips give him tummy ache

....

12. i am going to see my uncle tom will come with me

....

Capital letters and full stops
Revision page

> **Remember:**
> a sentence begins with a capital letter
> and ends with a full stop.
> The word 'I' is always a capital letter.
> Always use a capital letter for a name.

Add capital letters and full stops to the sentences below.
Some **of the examples have two sentences.**

1. yuri gagarin was the first man in space i read it in a book

....

2. i have lost my watch i cannot find it anywhere

....

3. the lights went out i had to find a candle

....

4. my teacher is called jean smith

....

5. i went for a picnic mum and jane came as well

....

6. imran and i went skating with sarah

....

7. stop at the crossing i can see a car coming

....

8. my baby sister is called grace elizabeth i like those names

....

9. my rabbit is called fluffy when he was small he was soft and fluffy

....

10. it is very late i think you should go to bed

....

Capital letters and full stops

> **Remember:**
> always use a capital letter for place names e.g. Japan, Paris
> and for nationalities* e.g. English, Chinese

Add capital letters and full stops to the sentences below.
Some of the examples have two sentences.

1. there are some very good ski slopes in austria

   ....

2. there are more sheep than people in new zealand

   ....

3. we went by ferry to france next time we shall use eurotunnel

   ....

4. i saw a programme about safari parks in kenya

   ....

5. there are fifty states in the united states of america

   ....

6. her father was born in italy her mother is dutch

   ....

7. one of the first railways in england ran from darlington to stockton

   ....

8. we visited the pyramids in egypt

   ....

9. canberra is the capital city of australia

   ....

10. my uncle is leaving africa and is going to china

   ....

11. it is raining in germany but it is sunny in belgium

   ....

* The meaning of nationality may need to be explained.

Capital letters and full stops
Revision page

Below are four sentences. Rewrite them, putting in the capital letters and the full stops.

athens is the capital city of greece the highest mountain in greece is called mount olympus olives, figs and other fruits are grown in greece we study the ancient greeks at school

....

....

....

....

....

Below are eight sentences. Rewrite them, putting in the capital letters and the full stops.

a castle is a fort most of the first castles in britain were built by the normans these castles were made of wood and earth they were often built on the top of a hill later castles were built of stone they were much stronger and had very thick walls sometimes a ditch was dug all round the castle this was filled with water and called a moat

....

....

....

....

....

....

....

....

....

Capital letters and full stops

Remember:
always use a capital letter for the name of:

a street or road   e.g. Rose Avenue

a building   e.g. Empire State Building

a train or bus station   e.g. Victoria Station

an airport   e.g. Heathrow Airport

an aunt or uncle   e.g. Uncle Fred

Add the capital letters and full stops.

1. peter lives in bridge street

....

2. i went to church road to visit auntie jess

....

3. we climbed to the top of the eiffel tower

....

4. they live in acorn avenue and we live in haddon road

....

5. we drove from bristol to cardiff

....

6. the tower of london is near tower bridge

....

Rewrite the sentences adding the capital letters.

i went on a plane to germany   ....

i went to the bus station in milton   ....

i left my house in mill street   ....

i went by bus to birmingham airport   ....

On a separate piece of paper put the sentences in the right order.

Capital letters and full stops

Rewrite the following sentences beginning each with a capital letter and ending with a full stop. You will need to keep some capital letters in other places, but use them only where necessary.

There are **five** sentences.

MY SISTER ALICE IS TWO SHE WENT SHOPPING WITH MY MOTHER MY MOTHER IS CALLED PAT WHILE THEY WERE SHOPPING ALICE ATE A WHOLE BAG OF RAISINS MY MUM SAID THIS HAD KEPT HER QUIET

....

....

....

....

....

....

Do the same below. There are **four** sentences.

MY NAME IS SAM I LIVE IN CARTER STREET, HONITON I HAVE A BROTHER CALLED JAMES AND A SISTER CALLED ANNE MY DAD WORKS IN EXETER

....

....

....

....

....

Do the same below. There are **four** sentences.

I WENT TO LONDON I MET MY COUSIN PHILIP HE TOOK ME TO SEE SAINT PAUL'S CATHEDRAL LATER WE WALKED UP THE MALL TO BUCKINGHAM PALACE

....

....

....

....

Capital letters and full stops

Rewrite the sentences below. Remember to put in **all** the full stops and use capital letters only where necessary.
There are **seven** sentences.

KOALAS COME FROM AUSTRALIA THEY FEED ON GUM LEAVES THEY NEVER DRINK WATER THEY GET THE JUICE FROM THE GUM LEAVES THEY LOOK VERY SWEET BUT THEY HAVE LONG SHARP CLAWS KOALAS USED TO BE HUNTED FOR THEIR FUR THEY ARE NOW PROTECTED ANIMALS

....

....

....

....

....

....

....

Do the same below. There are **ten** sentences.

I LIVE IN ASH DRIVE, OXFORD THE JOHN RADCLIFFE HOSPITAL IS NEAR OUR HOUSE I WENT ON A SCHOOL TRIP TO HOLLAND I WENT WITH MY CLASS WE WENT BY COACH AND BOAT MY TEACHER TOOK A BUCKET THIS WAS A GOOD IDEA BECAUSE WAYNE WAS SICK WE SAW LOTS OF FLOWERS AND WINDMILLS IN HOLLAND IT WAS VERY LATE WHEN WE GOT BACK TO OXFORD WE WERE ALL VERY TIRED

....

....

....

....

....

....

....

....

....

Capital letters and full stops

> **Remember:**
> always use a capital letter for:
> days of the week   e.g. Monday
> months of the year   e.g. December

Days of the week
Add the capital letters.

__ onday,   __uesday,   __ednesday,   __hursday,   __riday

__aturday,   __unday

On a separate sheet of paper write the days of the week without looking at this page.

Months of the year
Add the capital letters.

__anuary,   __ebruary,   __arch,   __pril,   __ay,   __une,   __uly,

__ugust,   __eptember,   __ctober,   __ovember,   __ecember

On a separate sheet of paper write the months of the year without looking at this page.

Quiz

Find the five months from the clues. Then find the day.

1. This month has only three letters.   ....

2. The tenth month   ....

3. Leaves fall and fireworks explode in   ....

4. Christmas comes in this month.   ....

5. Before September, but after July   ....

6. Use the first letter of each answer, add a
    a sixth letter and you will have a day of   ....
    the week.

Capital letters and full stops

Remember:
always use a capital letter for special days.
e.g. Christmas Day,   Easter Day,   Good Friday,
Ramadan,   Mother's Day,   Hanukkah,
Chinese New Year,   Diwali.

Add the capital letters and full stops.

1. we are going to the match on new year's day

....

2. next week we celebrate hanukkah

....

3. a service is held at our church on remembrance sunday

....

4. i think that easter is in march this year

....

5. gita told me that ramadan ended last week

....

6. the weather is hot at christmas in australia

....

7. i have bought my mother a rose for mother's day

....

8. people switch on lights in their homes to celebrate diwali

....

9. we have chocolate eggs on easter sunday

....

10. my birthday is on boxing day

....

11. thanksgiving day is in november

....

12. we are going away on august bank holiday monday

....

Capital letters and full stops

Remember:

always use a capital letter for:

titles of books	e.g. Black Beauty
titles of poems	e.g. The Jabberwocky
names of newspapers	e.g. Daily Mail
titles of plays, films and songs	e.g. The Lion King

Add the capital letters and full stops.

1. my mother reads roald dahl stories to me

....

2. at christmas we sang silent night

....

3. i have the video of pocahontas

....

4. we went to the royal albert hall to see the ballet called swan lake

....

Rewrite and complete the sentences below adding the capital letters and full stops.

5. i think my teacher reads the newspaper called

....

6. my favourite film is

....

7. the book i am reading is called

....

8. carl played the lead in our school play called

....

9. the famous singer sang

....

Capital letters and full stops

> **Remember:**
> always use a capital letter for titles:
> e.g.
>
> Princess Margaret   Sir Winston Churchill
> Saint Joan of Arc   President Mandela
> Doctor Jones   Mr. Green

Add the capital letters and full stops.

1. the queen is married to prince philip

....

2. doctor singh visited st john's school

....

3. king henry VIII had six wives

....

4. i saw the president of the united states

....

5. sir cliff richard is a famous pop star

....

6. lady thatcher was prime minister for many years

....

7. my mum has a friend called mrs carter

....

8. prince william and prince harry are brothers

....

9. saint george is the patron saint of england

....

10. the duchess of kent goes to the wimbledon lawn tennis championships

....

11. princess caroline is the daughter of princess grace of monaco

....

12 the reverend mrs joan watson is the new vicar of st mary's church

....

Capital letters and full stops

> **Remember:**
> if a title is <u>not</u> followed by a name, do <u>not</u> use a capital letter.
> e.g. Although <u>D</u>octor Jones lives next door, I go
> to see another <u>d</u>octor if I am ill.

Add the capital letters and full stops.

1. my doctor is called doctor burton

....

2. mr king played golf with major thomas

....

3. sir edmund hillary climbed mount everest

....

4. i think that nurse wilson will dress my bad leg

....

5. all the generals had dinner at general patton's house

....

6. the doctor came to visit my sister sofia

....

7. the duke and duchess of windsor lived in paris

....

8. the person sitting next to me is a captain

....

9. cleopatra was the queen of egypt

....

10. the friend of sherlock holmes was called doctor watson

....

11. we were very pleased to see deaconess morris in our church

....

Capital letters and full stops

> **Remember**
> the first letter of each line of a poem begins with a capital letter.
> Capital letters are used in the title of a poem.

Below is a poem by Robert Louis Stevenson.
Rewrite it, putting in the capital letters.

My Shadow

i have a little shadow that goes in and out with me
and what can be the use of him is more than i can see
he is very, very like me from the heels up to the head
and i see him jump before me, when i jump into my bed

the funniest thing about him is the way he likes to grow
not at all like proper children, which is always very slow
for he sometimes shoots up taller like an india rubber ball
and he sometimes gets so little that there's none of him at all

....
....
....
....
....
....
....
....
....

Rewrite the story below on another sheet, putting in all the capital letters and full stops. There are nine sentences.

mrs connors is very forgetful she was coming to see me on monday it was cold because it was december before she left the house she put her purse in the fridge and the butter in her pocket she marched down the road in her slippers and came to church street she spoke to the statue of prince william and passed the new wilson and collins shop i was very worried because she was late i took my dog bonzo and went with my friend doris to find her we saw her in the cinema queue waiting to see the film called lost in hyde park

Capital letters and full stops

Revision page

Add capital letters and full stops. *Some* **examples have two sentences.**

1. the statue of liberty is in new york

2. my favourite fruits are oranges and apples from south africa

3. mrs davey is a good and careful driver

4. you know that winnie the pooh likes honey i do as well

5. the old church of saint mark's is on the corner

6. i shall buy a box of belgian chocolates today

7. in august fred and sam met at the florida adventure park

8. my favourite aunt is called jane my favourite uncle is called frank

9. mother theresa died in the same year as princess diana

10. we went to hear elton john sing at the palladium

11. eros is a famous statue in piccadilly circus

12. i am going to spain next week i expect it will be hot

The question mark

> **Remember:**
>
> every question must end with a question mark.
>
> e.g. What is the time?

Rewrite the questions and add the question marks.

1. How are you

....

2. Where is he

....

3. Have you done your homework

....

Remember: the question mark finishes a question, so the next word must begin with a capital letter. e.g. How are you? I am well.

Add the capital letters, question marks and full stops. There is a question and answer on each line.

1. why is your sister crying she has lost her ball

....

2. can you swim i can almost swim

....

3. do you like fish we like fish very much

....

Rewrite the questions. Add a sentence to answer each question and remember to put in the capital letters, full stops and question marks.

1. where are you going

....

2. can you come to my party

....

3. which day shall we go for a picnic

....

The question mark

Special words can be used to introduce a question.

e.g. Where?   Where are you going?

Join the right question word in the box below to the right
matching words in order to make a question.
The first one is done for you.

Question words   **Matching words**

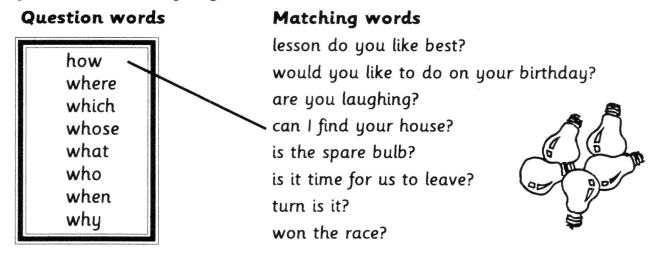

Question words	Matching words
how	lesson do you like best?
where	would you like to do on your birthday?
which	are you laughing?
whose	can I find your house?
what	is the spare bulb?
who	is it time for us to leave?
when	turn is it?
why	won the race?

**Write a question word at the beginning of each example below
in order to make a question.**

1. .... is your name?

2. .... are you feeling?

3. .... team will win the match?

4. .... did you stamp on his foot?

**You can turn a sentence into a question by changing the order of
the verb.   e.g. He is feeling better.   Is he feeling better?**

Change the sentences below into questions.

1. She has finished her homework.

....

2. They are going to the club tonight.

....

3. The coach will stop at Paradise Hotel.

....

4. The boy has put the stamps on the parcel.

....

The question mark

Write the question to each answer, putting in the question marks.

1. .... It's half-past two.

2. .... Yes, I took the dog out.

3. .... You go left at the church.

4. .... The cases are in the loft.

5. .... Yes, it is raining.

6. .... The garden tools are in the shed.

7. .... It would be nicer to go for a walk.

8. .... No, let's go skating instead.

Space it out.

Space out the words and put in the capital letters, full stops or question marks. The first one is done for you. You will find both a question and a sentence in 6 and 7.

1. canyoucometoseeournewpuppy

   Can you come to see our new puppy?

2. pleasemaywehaveadrinkoforange

....

3. didyouknowthatdrcarsonwenttoliveinspain

....

4. canyoucometomypartyonfriday

....

5. canyoushowmethestatueofwilliamblakeinbridgwater

....

6. whereisyourothershoeileftitinmybag

....

7. thatisoneofthewaystodoverdoyouknowanotherway

....

Capital letters, full stops and question marks
Revision page

What's wrong?

Correct the mistakes in the examples below.

1. do you know what time it is it is Half past two

   ....

2. i would like a Cup of tea? would you like one.

   ....

3. george watches blue Peter is it his Favourite programme

   ....

4. jenny is very fit she plays Tennis every day. at boston

   ....

5. i have lost my suitcase i must have left it. on the train?

   ....

6. in february. we went on a Skiing Holiday gina broke her leg

   ....

7. mrs white lent me a book. Called peter pan by james barrie

   ....

8. some camels have one hump and some have two humps?

   ....

9. we went to the Ho chi ming. chinese Restaurant on saturday

   ....

10. my cat Lucy. caught a mouse it upset me

   ....

11. her Birthday is in june? is yours in september

   ....

12. my doctor is called doctor luker his Surgery is in north road?

   ....

Capital letters, full stops and question marks
Revision page

Correct the mistakes in the following story.
You may like to use a red pen.

last wednesday mum and dad took wesley and me to france for the day we sailed from dover early in the morning on the ferry called seajoy captain edwards welcomed us all on board

mum saw her friend doctor mason in the lounge she told us that sir patrick arnold was on the top deck dad said that sir patrick was a very famous composer who lived in brighton

just before we arrived in calais the captain asked if there was a doctor on board doctor mason bandaged the leg of a little girl who had fallen down the stairs

when we arrived in france we went to a cafe called maison rouge wesley and i had a huge plate of frites it was then time to go to the supermarket mum and dad bought lots of food including some camembert cheese and some french wine we bought a kilo of french peaches and wesley and i ate one straight away

we were so busy that we forgot the time and nearly missed the ferry i am glad we caught it because on the way back we asked sir patrick for his autograph i will show it to my uncle ron when he comes to see us

Answer page

N.B. (i) There may be an occasion where a comma or inverted commas would normally be used but as the book concentrates on full stops, the commas and inverted commas have generally been omitted.

(ii) Abbreviations that include the first and last letters of a word are equally acceptable with or without the full stops e.g. Dr or Dr.

(iii) Capital letters for 'mum' and 'dad' are optional but lower case is used in this book.

Page 3.

1. My cat likes to drink milk. 2. We often go camping in the holidays. 3. There are thirty children in my class. 4. It was too cold to swim in the sea. 5. We think that there are mice in our loft. 6. One day we all went for a bicycle ride. 7. Sometimes it snows in winter. 8. My friend cut her finger on the knife. 9. We had a lovely time at the fair. 10. It is dangerous to play with matches. 11. We are going for a long walk today. 12. My sister likes to use the computer.

Page 4

1. It is too late. You cannot go out now. 2. Turn the music down. It is too loud. 3. It is cold today. We will need our coats. 4. The horse stepped on my foot. It broke my toe. 5. My friend is coming home today. We are going to meet her. 6. Blow out the match. It will burn your finger. 7. We did our homework. We played football later. 8. Put the ice cream in the fridge. It will melt. 9. My pen is blue. His pen is black. 10. Our dog was naughty. He chewed my slipper. 11. Today is a holiday. We hope that it will not rain. 12. I looked out of the window. I saw a fox in the garden.

Page 5.

1. There are many books on the shelf. 2. We are late. We must run to catch the train. 3. It is a lovely day today and the sun is shining. 4. The telephone is ringing. It could be my friend calling. 5. We went to see a ghost film. We were all frightened. 6. Our team won the cup. We were very pleased. 7. My grandma is very helpful and kind. 8. The class went jogging to keep fit. 9. The doctor came to see my sister. She had chickenpox. 10. My brother spilt some ink on the carpet. My mother was cross. 11. The headteacher read a poem. It was very funny. 12. The ambulance went past. The blue light was flashing.

Page 6.

Elephants have trunks. They do not use their trunks like straws. They fill only the tips of their trunks with water. They spray the water into their mouths.

A whale is a mammal. There are eighty kinds of whale. An adult sperm whale may have a brain which weighs nine kilograms. We do not know if this means that the whale is very clever.

The moon is smaller than the sun. It looks sp big as the sun because it is closer to us. The moon is even smaller than the earth. It takes almost a month for the moon to go round the earth. We get the word month from the word moon.

Page 7.

1. The book I want to borrow is not on the shelf. 2. He told me that I was good at football. 3. That is the game I would like for my computer. 4. I ran very fast in the race. 5. I told my friend that I could go to her house for tea. 6. You know that I am good at ice skating. 7. If I buy a bag of popcorn I can share it with you. 8. I need a drink because I am thirsty 9. I love to ride on the roller coaster and the big wheel. 10. I have a large collection of marbles. 11. My brother said that I could ride his new bicycle. 12. I like to watch the dolphins jump.

Page 8.

1. I can go to the park when it stops raining. 2. I always wear blue shoes. 3. I must hurry. I might be late for the dentist. 4. I can go to the party. 5. He read that book. I read it first. 6. I love cakes. She likes cheese. 7. I must not forget the way. I have to turn right at the fire station. 8. I must not shout. 9. I made a very good poster for the school disco. 10. I overslept and I missed the train. 11. I caught a huge fish. It won the prize. 12. I must not jump in the water. It is very deep.

Page 9

1. I put on my music. John did not like it. 2. We went to the fair. I had a ride with Shahab on the dodgems. 3. I go to school on the bus. Ann walks to school. 4. Please come to my house. It is Harry's birthday. 5. I had lunch with Gill. David did not. 6. The bell rang. Maria ran to open the door. 7. Linda began to play the trumpet. Peter left the room. 8. My friend Sarah has two hamsters. They have very sharp teeth. 9. I am going skating. Janet said that she would come too. 10. That house is said to have a ghost. Cheryl and I do not believe in ghosts. 11. Marcus loves fish. Chips give him tummy ache. 12. I am going to see my uncle. Tom will come with me.

Page 10

1. Yuri Gagarin was the first man in space. I read it in a book. 2. I have lost my watch. I cannot find it anywhere. 3. The lights went out. I had to find a candle. 4. My teacher is called Jean Smith. 5. I went for a picnic. Mum and Jane came as well. 6. Imran and I went skating with Sarah 7. Stop at the crossing. I can see a car coming. 8. My baby sister is called Grace Elizabeth. I like those names. 9. My rabbit is called Fluffy. When he was small he was soft and fluffy. 10. It is very late. I think you should go to bed.

Page 11

1. There are some very good ski slopes in Austria. 2. There are more sheep than people in New Zealand. 3. We went by ferry to France. Next time we shall use Eurotunnel. 4. I saw a programme about safari parks in Kenya. 5. There are fifty states in the United States of America. 6. Her father was born in Italy. Her mother is Dutch. 7. One of the first railways in England ran from Darlington to Stockton. 8. We visited the pyramids in Egypt. 9. Canberra is the capital city of Australia. 10. My uncle is leaving Africa and is going to China. 11. It is raining in Germany but it is sunny in Belgium.

Answer page (cont.)

Page 12

Athens is the capital city of Greece. The highest mountain in Greece is called Mount Olympus. Olives, figs and other fruits are grown in Greece. We study the Ancient Greeks at school.

A castle is a fort. Most of the first castles in Britain were built by the Normans. These castles were made of wood and earth. They were often built on the top of a hill. Later castles were built of stone. They were much stronger and had very thick walls. Sometimes a ditch was dug all round the castle. This was filled with water and called a moat.

Page 13

1. Peter lives in Bridge Street. 2. I went to Church Road to visit Auntie Jess. 3. We climbed to the top of the Eiffel Tower. 4. They live in Acorn Avenue and we live in Haddon Road. 5. We drove from Bristol to Cardiff. 6. The Tower of London is near Tower Bridge.

I left my house in Mill Street. I went to the bus station in Milton. I went by bus to Birmingham Airport. I went on a plane to Germany.

Page 14

My sister Alice is two. She went shopping with my mother. My mother is called Pat. While they were shopping Alice ate a whole bag of raisins. My mum said this had kept her quiet.

My name is Sam. I live in Carter Street, Honiton. I have a brother called James and a sister called Anne. My dad works in Exeter.

I went to London. I met my cousin Philip. He took me to see Saint Paul's Cathedral. Later we walked up The Mall to Buckingham Palace.

Page 15

Koalas come from Australia. They feed on gum leaves. They never drink water. They get the juice from the gum leaves. They look very sweet but they have long sharp claws. Koalas used to be hunted for their fur. They are now protected animals.

I live in Ash Drive, Oxford. The John Radcliffe Hospital is near our house. I went on a school trip to Holland. I went with my class. We went by coach and boat. My teacher took a bucket. This was a good idea because Wayne was sick. We saw lots of flowers and windmills in Holland. It was very late when we got back to Oxford. We were all very tired.

Page 16 Quiz

1. May 2. October 3. November 4. December 5. August 6. Monday.

Page 17

1. We are going to the match on New Year's Day. 2. Next week we celebrate Hanukkah. 3. A service is held at our church on Remembrance Sunday. 4. I think that Easter is in March this year. 5. Gita told me that Ramadan ended last week. 6. The weather is hot at Christmas in Australia. 7. I have bought my mother a rose for Mother's Day. 8. People switch on lights in their homes to celebrate Diwali. 9. We have chocolate eggs on Easter Sunday. 10. My birthday is on Boxing Day. 11. Thanksgiving Day is in November. 12. We are going away on August Bank Holiday Monday.

Page 18

1. My mother reads Roald Dahl stories to me. 2. At Christmas we sang Silent Night. 3. I have the video of Pocahontas. 4. We went to the Royal Albert Hall to see the ballet called Swan Lake.

Page 19

1. The Queen is married to Prince Philip. 2. Doctor Singh visited St John's School. 3. King Henry VIII had six wives. 4. I saw the President of the United States. 5. Sir Cliff Richard is a famous pop star. 6. Lady Thatcher was Prime Minister for many years. 7. My mum has a friend called Mrs. Carter. 8. Prince William and Prince Harry are brothers. 9. Saint George is the patron saint of England. 10. The Duchess of Kent goes to the Wimbledon Lawn Tennis Championships. 11. Princess Caroline is the daughter of Princess Grace of Monaco. 12. The Reverend Mrs. Joan Watson is the new vicar of St. Mary's Church.

Page 20

1. My doctor is called Doctor Burton. 2. Mr King played golf with Major Thomas. 3. Sir Edmund Hillary climbed Mount Everest. 4. I think that Nurse Wilson will dress my bad leg. 5. All the generals had dinner at General Patton's house. 6. The doctor came to visit my sister Sofia. 7. The Duke and Duchess of Windsor lived in Paris. 8. The person sitting next to me is a captain. 9. Cleopatra was the Queen of Egypt. 10. The friend of Sherlock Holmes was called Doctor Watson. 11. We were very pleased to see Deaconess Morris in our church.

Page 21

My Shadow

I have a little shadow that goes in and out with me
And what can be the use of him is more than I can see.
He is very, very like me from the heels up to the head
And I see him jump before me, when I jump into my bed.

The funniest thing about him is the way he likes to grow
Not at all like proper children, which is always very slow
For he sometimes shoots up taller like an india rubber ball
And he sometimes gets so little that there's none of him at all.

Answer page (cont.)

Page 21 (cont.)

Mrs. Connors is very forgetful. She was coming to see me on Monday. It was cold because it was December. Before she left the house she put her purse in the fridge and the butter in her pocket. She marched down the road in her slippers and came to Church Street. She spoke to the statue of Prince William and passed the new Wilson and Collins shop. I was very worried because she was late. I took my dog Bonzo and went with my friend Doris to find her. We saw her in the cinema queue waiting to see the film called Lost in Hyde Park.

Page 22

1. The Statue of Liberty is in New York. 2. My favourite fruits are oranges and apples from South Africa. 3. Mrs. Davey is a good and careful driver. 4. You know that Winnie the Pooh likes honey. I do too. 5. The old church of Saint Mark's is on the corner. 6. I shall buy a box of Belgian chocolates today. 7. In August Fred and Sam met at the Florida Adventure Park. 8. My favourite aunt is called Jane. My favourite uncle is called Frank. 9. Mother Teresa died in the same year as Princess Diana. 10. We went to hear Elton John sing at the Palladium. 11. Eros is a famous statue in Piccadilly Circus. 12. I am going to Spain next week. I expect it will be hot.

Page 23

1. How are you? 2. Where is he? 3. Have you done your homework?
1. Why is your sister crying? She has lost her ball. 2. Can you swim? I can almost swim. 3. Do you like fish? We like fish very much.

Page 24

1. **Where** is the spare bulb? 2. **Which** lesson do you like best? 3. **Whose** turn is it? 4. **What** would you like to do on your birthday? 5. **Who** won the race? 6. **When** is it time for us to leave? 7. **Why** are you laughing?
1. What is your name? 2. How are you feeling? 3. Which team will win the match? 4. Why did you stamp on his foot?
1. Has she finished her homework? 2. Are they going to the club tonight? 3. Will the coach stop at Paradise Hotel? 4. Has the boy put the stamps on the parcel?

Page 25 (top) There will be variations on these answers.

1. What is the time? 2. Did you take the dog out? 3. Which way do I go? 4. Where are the cases? 5. Is it raining? 6. Where did you put the garden tools? 7. Shall we watch a video? 8. Shall we go swimming?

Page 25 (bottom)

2. Please may we have a drink of orange? 3. Did you know that Dr. Carson went to live in Spain? 4. Can you come to my party on Friday? 5. Can you show me the statue of William Blake in Bridgwater? 6. Where is your other shoe? I left it in my bag. 7. That is one of the ways to Dover. Do you know another way?

Page 26

1. Do you know what time it is? It is half past two. 2. I would like a cup of tea. Would you like one? 3. George watches Blue Peter. Is it his favourite programme? 4. Jenny is very fit. She plays tennis every day at Boston. 5. I have lost my suitcase. I must have left it on the train. 6. In February we went on a skiing holiday. Gina broke her leg. 7. Mrs. White lent me a book called Peter Pan by James Barrie. 8. Some camels have one hump and some have two humps. 9. We went to the Ho Chi Ming Chinese restaurant on Saturday. 10. My cat Lucy caught a mouse. It upset me. 11. Her birthday is in June. Is yours in September? 11. My doctor is called Doctor Luker. His surgery is in North Road.

Page 27

Last Wednesday mum and dad took Wesley and me to France for the day. We sailed from Dover early in the morning on the ferry called Seajoy. Captain Edwards welcomed us all on board.

Mum saw her friend Doctor Mason in the lounge. She told us that Sir Patrick Arnold was on the top deck. Dad said that Sir Patrick was a very famous composer who lived in Brighton.

Just before we arrived in Calais the captain asked if there was a doctor on board. Doctor Mason bandaged the leg of a little girl who had fallen down the stairs.

When we arrived in France we went to a cafe called Maison Rouge. Wesley and I had a huge plate of frites. It was then time to go to the supermarket. Mum and dad bought lots of food including some Camembert cheese and some French wine. We bought a kilo of French peaches and Wesley and I ate one straight away.

We were so busy that we forgot the time and nearly missed the ferry. I am glad we caught it because on the way back we asked Sir Patrick for his autograph. I will show it to my Uncle Ron when he comes to see us.